A Panda Paperback

contents

The author

Maurice Pipard is a school teacher with a difference. He prefers games and the informality of recreational activities to classroom teaching. He is one of the people responsible for the ''open schools'' in France, and devotes a great deal of his time to the planning of leisure activities for children's clubs and summer camps.

Illustrations by Nicole Claveloux

Published in 1975 by Franklin Watts, Inc., New York, N.Y.

Illustrations copyright © 1974 Editions Gallimard, Paris
Printed in France

ISBN: 0-531-02733-3
Library of Congress Catalog Card Number: 74-3507

GAMES FOR A RAINY DAY

Franklin Watts, Inc.
New York, 1975

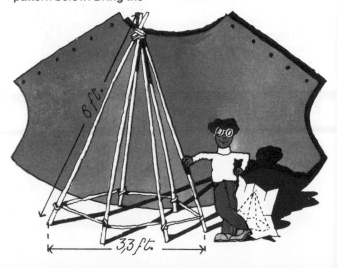

playhouses

a tepee

This tepee is light, and easy to make and store.

What you need

- 6 wooden poles about 5 to 6½ feet long
- A ball of strong string
- Some material or stiff wrapping paper. (Have fun decorating it beforehand.)

Look at the diagram below: A firm knot holds the poles together at the top; the poles spread out at the bottom making a circular base about 3¼ feet in diameter; cord is strung between the poles to keep them in place. Cut out the material following the measurements on the pattern below. Bring the straight edges together so that the holes match; thread string through each pair of holes and tie securely. Slip the whole thing over the wooden frame.

6 ft.

3,3 ft.

Wind the string several times around the top of the sticks, and then thread it in and out between each one as shown in the diagram.

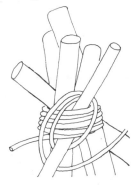

the table tent

The table top is your roof. All you need to do is add walls, windows, and a door!

What you need
- A wooden table

- A roll of material or stiff paper. The width of the material or paper should be the same as the height of the table; the length should be equal to all four sides of the table added together, minus about 18 inches for the door. Fasten the material to the edge of the table with thumbtacks or masking tape. Now you can decorate the walls and cut out the windows.

a corrugated castle

Now you can build your own dream house. It can be anything from a fortress with towers, a drawbridge, and perhaps even a dungeon to an ultramodern open-air house. It does not rain in your room, so who needs a roof?

Your building materials
• Some big rolls of corrugated cardboard at least 3 feet wide.
• A pair of sharp scissors.
• Some paint and a paintbrush.

Down to work
If you want to make a tower you will need a piece of cardboard about 6 feet long. Roll it up so that the two ends touch, and join them as shown. Cut out loopholes, windows, and doors with the scissors, and add a few finishing touches with a paintbrush.

This is how you join together the walls of the tower. Fit the tabs (B) into the slots (A) and fold them back to keep them in place.

crazy
cardboard
houses

Cardboard boxes, like houses, come in all shapes and sizes. If you are lucky enough to find one that once housed a refrigerator or gas range, you will be able to move in right away. Let yourself in by the front door with a pair of scissors, and cut out a window or two to let in the light. If you want shutters on your house, cut out only three sides of the window and fold the cardboard back along the fourth side. You can reinforce the hinges with a strip of masking tape, or paper and glue. Now decide what your house is to be—a sentry box, a grocery store, a doll house, or a kennel. The smaller the cardboard boxes, the more you need. Why not make yourself an igloo? Stack the boxes in layers and stick them together with masking tape to keep them from tumbling down. You can

give extra support to the roof by laying flat wooden slats under the top layer of boxes. Paint the whole thing white, and you will have a warm, welcoming abode in which to dream away a long winter's afternoon.

For green thumbs only

bottled plants

Bottling plants is rather like bottling fruit: by preserving them in a bottle, you can enjoy them all year round, and not just when they are in season. The plants may not be good to eat, but they do brighten up your room on a rainy day. They can live in any closed container, provided it is transparent. This is because the oxygen and the water within the container are constantly regenerated in a sort of closed circuit. This is exactly what happens in a greenhouse (on a larger scale, of course).

Fruit, vegetables, and flowers can be made to grow under glass at any time of the year. By regulating the temperature inside the greenhouse and the amount of light coming in from outside, it is possible to simulate almost any climate in the world. (You could even grow bananas at the North Pole if you wanted to!) This artificial "mini-climate" is known as a *micro-climate.* The Climatron in Saint Louis, Missouri, is the most unusual greenhouse in the world. It covers an area of well over a square mile. It is more than 70 feet high and has a huge domed roof, $\frac{1}{4}$-inch thick, made out of plexiglass. More than 1500 different species of plants are grown in the Climatron. Some of the tallest trees inside, such as the South American Balsa (from which model airplanes are made), are almost as tall as the building itself. The Climatron has an elaborate system of aeration, which provides both ventilation and humidity where needed. It also has an artificial sun and moon. All these devices make it possible to reproduce a huge variety of climatic conditions from all over the world: the damp heat of the Amazon forest, the dry heat of the Sahara, the ocean breezes of Hawaii. The plants and vegetation of each region thrive in their own specially created micro-climate.

First the bottle
Find a transparent glass or plastic container (jam jar, flower vase, etc.). The opening or neck should be as narrow as possible, to prevent too much water from evaporating. Clean it thoroughly before you begin.

Then the earth
The earth should be of very good quality. A mixture of sand, peat, and leaf mold does very well (you will find these in any gardening shop). You need very little of each.

And last of all the plants
Choose *non-flowering* plants that grow rather slowly, like the ones on the next page. They must be very small to start with. Why not put several different plants in the same bottle and make a miniature garden? Select each one carefully

11

according to its size and shape.

Green fingers
Use a funnel to drop the earth into the jar (see

diagram 1). A layer 1½ to 2-inches deep is all you need. Arrange your plants on the table beside the jar in the positions you want

1

2

3

them to occupy (taking
into account the size of the
jar).
Now you can start
planting: Use a stick or
wooden spoon handle to
make the holes in the earth
for each plant, starting in
the middle and working
out (2).

Lower one plant
carefully into its hole.
Leave some of the earth
around its roots to give it
extra weight (3).

Turn it so that it faces
the way you want it to.

Use your stick to flatten

the earth around the plant.

Once the plant is firmly embedded, take a piece of wire with a hooked end, and straighten out the leaves (4).

Spoon a little water into the jar (5).

Put the jar somewhere out of the sun. Your plant needs light, but it does not need to be fried!
Now, sit back and watch your garden grow!

An unfailing remedy for boredom

card tricks

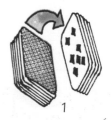

Take a pack of cards and remove all the cards from 2 through 6 (you now have 32 cards left). Hold the pack with the 32 cards face down in your left hand, and start cutting it in different places with your right hand until one of your friends says "Stop." Ask him to take the card on the top of the pile in your left hand, look at it, and put it back (without showing it to you, of course). Turn the cards over one by one until you recognize the right one. **It can't fail**—because while your friend was looking at his card, you took a quick look at the card at the bottom of the pile of cards in your right hand (in this case the 7 of Diamonds—see sketch 1). Your friend's card goes back into the pack *under* the 7 of Diamonds—so when you turn up the cards one by one, *his* card will be the one *after* the 7. Easy, isn't it?

A variation:

This time when the card has been put back into the pack where it came from, you turn the pack over so that the cards are now right side up. Lay them out one by one on the table in two rows of 16 cards each. As you do so, locate the

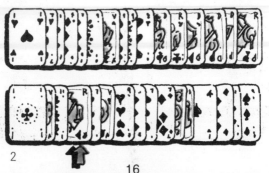

2

16

3

other person's card (it is the one *before* the 7 of Diamonds because the pack is now the other way up—see sketch 2). You now know which the card is, **but you do not say so.** You now ask him to pick one of the rows of cards. If his card *is* in the row he chooses, you say "Right, I will keep these cards." But if he chooses the row without his card in it, you say, "I'll put these away then." **Either way his card will remain on the table.** Now turn each card over in turn and number them out loud from left to right, and from 1 to 16 (make a mental note of where the other person's card is— ninth from the left in sketch 2). Ask your friend to choose a number from 1 to 16.

If he names the number of the card (9), you turn the card up right away (what a master stroke!).

If the number he chooses is *lower* than the number of his card (9), you remove all the cards to the *left* of the number he has given; if it is *higher*, you remove all the cards to the *right* of the number he gives. Now, suppose you have 12 cards left. You can turn them up in four rows of three (as in sketch 3), number them, and go on removing cards as before until there are only three left (the correct one and two others). Number the last three cards 1, 2, and 3. Invite the person to choose a number from 1 to 3. If he chooses 1, you pick up his card, saying, "the first card is *yours.*" If he picks 3, you pick up the other two first, and then his.

The secret: You know the other person's card right from the beginning, and you make sure it stays on the table while you remove the others.

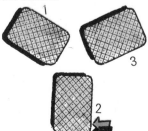

keep them guessing

If you want to keep everybody guessing, try this card trick. You can take in as many as ten people at one time. (You really need at least two other people to make it interesting—ten is the maximum.)

You take 20 cards (any ones you like) and set them out face down on the table in piles of two. You ask each person to choose a pile, to look at the two cards, and to remember them. You then collect the cards in pairs (but not in any particular order—and without looking at them of course!). You set them out on the table, face up this time, in four rows with five cards in each.

Now you ask each person in turn to tell you which rows his cards are in. After a moment's thought, you will be able to tell each person which his cards are.

How did you do it?
The secret lies in these four magic words:

CALAS

RICOR

POPUL

TITUS

If you look closely at the words you will see that they are made up of ten different letters of the alphabet. You will also notice that each of the ten letters appears twice. Now you must memorize the words. When you put the cards on the table the second time, you must

have a clear mental picture of the words in your head. What you do is to "write" the words with your pairs of cards. Each pair corresponds to one of the ten letters in the magic words. The first two are the C's, the second two are the A's, and so on. When the person tells you which rows his cards are in, you can work out which letters they correspond to. Have another close look at the four magic words. If he says the first and second rows, you know that his cards must be the C's (the only letters the first two lines of the formula have in common—see diagram). If he says they are both in the first row, they must be the A's. If he says the first and third rows, they must be the L's; the second and fourth rows the I's, first and fourth the S's. Learn the four magic words by heart and practice setting

out the cards in the right order before you try this trick out on your friends. If you think they are getting a bit too close to discovering your secret, you can always change your magic words. Try these four instead:

BRIAR

STOAT

BULLS

UNION

They work just as well.

19

your turn to guess

Instead of the others always picking the cards, pick one yourself and make *them* do the guessing.
Take a card from the pack, look at it and put it away where nobody can see it. Now start asking another person questions.

For example: Penny picks the Jack of Hearts from the pack. Somehow she has got to force Peter to "choose" that card.

What does she do? She says, "In a pack, you have red cards and black ones. Which do you want?" Peter says, "Red." That is helpful because the Jack of Hearts is red, but if he had chosen black, Penny would simply have said, "That leaves us with the reds," and gone on from there. "In the reds you have hearts and diamonds. Which do you choose?" Peter chooses diamonds and Penny says, "Good. That leaves us with hearts. Hearts it is. Now in each suit there are picture cards and ordinary cards—which do you want?" "Picture cards." "Right. There are gentleman picture cards and lady picture cards—which will you have?" "Ladies," answers Peter. "That leaves us with the men. Which will you have —the King or the Jack?" "The King." "That leaves us with the Jack—the Jack of Hearts it is! Well done!" says Penny.
Suppose Penny had picked a number card (the 7) instead of the Jack. She would have asked Peter to choose between even and odd numbers. Then she would have said: "In the odd numbers you have numbers below 5 and numbers above it." . . . "Numbers below 7 and above 7" and so on until only the 7 remained. She would have forced him to choose the right color and suit just as in the first example above.

find fourteen

The Jack counts 11.
- The Queen counts 12.
- The King counts 13.

The combinations you need are, therefore, King and Ace, Queen and 2,

This is a game of Solitaire to play on your own or with some friends. Each person must have his own pack of cards.

Set out eight cards face down on the table, in two rows of four cards each. You are allowed to turn up only two cards at a time.

The object of the game is to get rid of as many cards as possible by pairing them up. You are allowed to do this only if the two together add up to 14.

- The Ace counts as 1.
- The cards from 2 to 10 count as their number values.

Jack and 3, and so on. If your cards do not add up to 14, you turn them face down again and try two more. If they *do* add up to 14, you pick them up and put them to one side. Then take two more cards from the pack and put them in the empty spaces. Go on from where you left off.

You win if you succeed in pairing up all the cards, that is to say, you have no more cards left at the end.

You lose if you find you cannot get rid of any more cards, and still have eight cards on the table and more in your pack.

If there are several of you playing at once, the first one to get rid of all his cards is the winner. (If you get stuck, shuffle the cards and start all over again.)

The cards in drawing 1 add up to 14 and can be put aside; the cards in drawing 2 have to be turned face down again.

matchmaking

A good matchmaker needs a good memory (and a little bit of luck thrown in!). Two people play at a time. Take a pack of cards and remove all the cards from 2 through 6 (this leaves you with 32). Shuffle the pack of 32 cards well and set them out in four rows of eight. Take turns to turn up two cards at a time from anywhere in the four rows.
• If your two cards "match," you pick them up, and it is your turn to play again.
• If they do not match, you must turn them over and leave them where they are. It is your opponent's turn to play.

What is a "match"?
Any two cards which have the same value (two eights, two Jacks, two Aces . . .) *or* a King and a Queen (*two* Kings or *two* Queens would be bound to fight!). When all the cards have been matched, you each count the number of pairs you have succeeded in making. *The best matchmaker* is the one with the most cards.

speaking of cards

Where do playing cards come from? No one is absolutely certain, but it seems that they were first heard of in Europe around the beginning of the fifteenth century and that they were introduced via the Orient.

They may be related to the game of chess. Whereas the King and Queen have kept their identity, the chess castle became the Ace; the Knight became the Jack; and the pawns became the numbered cards.

The four suits—Spades, Hearts, Diamonds, and Clubs—probably originated in France and represented four different levels of society.

Spades (from the Spanish word *espada,* meaning a spear) were warriors and soldiers.

Hearts represented religion—the Church and priests—and the life of the soul.

Diamonds represented the merchants.

Clubs represented the serfs and peasants. ("Club-men" were bands of peasants who carried clubs and resisted both Cavaliers and Roundheads in Cromwellian times in England.)

In many card games Spades are still the strongest suit, and Clubs the weakest.

capture the cork

Challenge your friends to a round of "capture the cork." You need a cork, a yard of string, and a plastic drinking glass. Any small unbreakable container will do.

Kneel or crouch on the floor opposite each other. One of you holds the string with the cork tied to one end, and the other holds the glass poised about 4 inches above the cork, ready to strike.

On "go," the person with the glass tries to pop the glass over the cork before his opponent has time to jerk it away.

Be quick, be nimble . . .

topple-me-over

If you have a lot of energy to spare, what about a game of topple-me-over? Crouch on the floor opposite a friend with the palms of your hands pressed against his. On ''go'' you start to try and throw the other person off balance:

• You are allowed to use only the palms of your hands, and you must not touch the other person anywhere else.

• You can leap forwards and backwards (always in a crouched position).

• You can part palms and then attack again.

You lose

• If you topple over.

• If you stand up.

• If you deliberately take away your hands just as the other person is about to attack.

In the left-hand drawing below, B is the loser. In the right-hand drawing A is the loser (he took his hands away).

bodies

This game is a slightly different version of an old favorite that you probably all know (a piece of paper is passed from player to player and the first person draws the head of a figure, the second draws the neck, the third, the arms and so on). This time let your imagination run wild and *draw anything that comes into your head.* You need at least two people to play but not more than six at a time. If there are several players, tape a few sheets together so that everyone will have enough room.

Make sure each person has a pencil. Start to draw at one end of the sheet of paper. Be careful not to use up more than your share of the space. When you have finished, fold the paper so that only a very small part of your drawing shows, and hand it to the person sitting next to you. He must fit his drawing next to yours, and so on, until there is no more room on the sheet.

Now—unfold the sheet and see what strange and comic creations emerge.

bodies in words

This written version of "Bodies" can be played in all sorts of different ways, but the basic idea is always the same: one person starts writing, and the next carries on from where he left off.

grammatical bodies

You all write in turn on the same sheet, folding it each time to hide what you have written. Decide beforehand that the first person is to write a noun, the second a verb, the third an adverb, and so on (in any combination you like) until the sentence is complete.

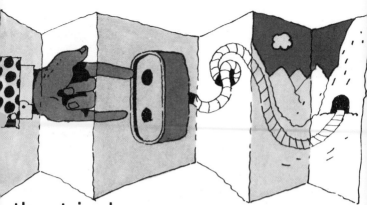

theatrical bodies

This time the body will be a play. Decide on a setting first of all. For example: three children with their dog have been left on their own overnight in a small farm miles from anywhere —what happens? You each choose a different character, and you write that character's part. Everyone starts writing at once. When you fold the paper you leave the last line of what you have written showing to give the next person an idea of how to continue. Some characters may have lots to say and others very little, so simply exchange papers with anyone who happens to be ready at the same time as you. When everyone has finished, compare the different versions of your "play" and decide which one is best.

a poetic body

For the poets among you, what about a body in verse? Write a few lines (or more if you feel inspired), fold the paper so that what you have written is completely hidden. Make a note of the rhymes and the number of syllables you have used at the foot of the page. The next person has to try to carry on in the same vein, using at least one of the rhymes and the same number of syllables. These bodies can take on any shape or form you like to give them—they will always be a surprise!

Think big

checkers with a difference

Does your kitchen or bathroom floor have square tiles? If so, it will

make an ideal giant checkerboard. Mark out the area you are going to play in (10 squares by 10) with chalk (but first make sure that the chalk wipes off easily with a damp cloth!). It does not matter if the tiles are all the same color; just take a piece of chalk and put a cross in all the "white" ones on your board.

Your 40 checker pieces will need to be giant-sized too. You can make them out of flat stones or boxes painted in bright colors, or use knives and forks, or even your baby brother's building blocks.

One more possibility: Let your checker pieces be a surprise—nice or nasty—a candy, a cooky, a pretty marble, or a paper clip. Wrap each one up in a small piece of colored paper. Each time you take one of your opponent's pieces, you unwrap it and see what it is. At the end of the game you can keep any checkers you have left over—so don't make all your surprises nasty ones!

giant chess

If you like to play chess why not make yourself a set of giant chess pieces to use on a tiled floor? The size you make the 32 different pieces depends on the size of the tiles. You can make some of them out of strips of wire bent into shape (like the Knight in the drawing), and others out of stiff cardboard. Cut out the shape you want and make a firm base by folding back the cardboard at the bottom and weighting it with a flat piece of wood, stone, or metal. Alternatively, roll the cardboard into a cone or cylinder, or use cardboard boxes or cans of different shapes which you can paint in bright colors. Have fun inventing all sorts of colorful designs.

Mark off your board with chalk (eight squares by eight), and when you are ready—into battle!

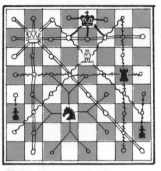

the game of chess

If you don't already know how to play chess, here is a brief summary of the rules . . .
Chess is a game for two. The chessboard is a square grid consisting of eight vertical rows by eight horizontal rows, 64 squares in all, which are alternately black and white in color. Each player has 16 pieces: 8 pawns, 2 castles, 2 knights, 2 bishops, a king and a queen.

The object of the game is to capture your opponent's king by trapping it in such a way, that no matter where it moves, you can still take it with one of your pieces. In chess, this is what is known as Check-Mate.

The moves each piece can make:
All the pieces except for the pawns can move both forwards and backwards. Look at the diagram above: the *castle* can move any distance up, down or across the board in a straight line (not diagonally). The *bishop* can move any distance on the diagonal. The *knight's* move is L-shaped; two squares in either a horizontal or vertical direction and then one square to its right or left. The *queen* can move any distance up, down, across or on the diagonal. The *king* can also move in any direction, but only one square at a time. The *pawns* can move only one square at a time *up* the board (except at their first turn, when each one has the choice of moving one or two squares). The knight is the only piece

that can jump over other pieces in its way but it can only capture an opponent's piece on the square it finally lands on.

"Capturing" pieces

If one of your opponent's pieces is in a square which one of your own pieces can occupy, you remove it from the board, putting your own piece in its place. Pawns are the only pieces which take in a direction other than the one in which they normally advance. They "capture" on the diagonal to left or right of the square in front of them.

At the beginning of the game, the pieces are arranged as shown in the diagram. These are just the basic rules of chess—it's up to you to find out more about this complex and fascinating game on your own!

unlikely chess lore

According to a well-known legend, the game of chess was invented by a Hindu priest by the name of Sissa. He wished to prove to the young prince, who was his pupil, that a King is powerless without his subjects.
The prince was most impressed and asked Sissa what he would like as a reward. This was the wise old man's reply: "I should like grains of corn—one on the first square of the chessboard, two on the second one, four on the third, and so on, the number of grains doubling from one square to the next, right up to the last square on the board [the sixty-fourth]."

This apparently humble request was granted— which goes to show that in legends nothing is impossible. In fact, there would not be nearly enough corn in the whole world (let alone in India) to reward the Hindu priest. Work it out for yourself!

For word whizzes

the dictionary game

Any number of people can play this word-guessing game. You need one dictionary and enough pencils and sheets of paper to go around.
One of you takes the dictionary and looks through it until he finds an unusual word which he thinks the others will not know. The rest of you have to write down what you think the word means. Though you probably won't know the meaning try and make your definition sound as convincing as possible. Meanwhile the "dictionary-person" writes the correct meaning on his own sheet of paper. He collects all the other sheets, shuffles them, and reads them out loud.
Listen carefully, and then vote for the definition you think is correct.
You score 1 point if you vote for the correct definition and 5 points if someone else votes for the one you made up.

anagrams galore

Choose a word with not less than six letters and look at it carefully. A great number of different words can be formed using the letters in that word. How many can you find? (They must be words of three letters or more.)

You can play this game by yourself or with a group of friends. Set yourselves a time limit and compare results at the end.

For example
PATIENCE

3 letters	4 letters
pat	nice
eat	pain
can	pint
ice	pact
ant	pine
pie	neat
tin	tape

5 letters	6 letters
paint	entice
antic	
enact	
pence	

There are quite a few more still hiding. Can you find them?

the family newsletter

Drawing on the wall is frowned on in most families, but why not have *one* wall in the house where *everyone* can write or draw? Hang up a large sheet of paper, and wait for the news items to flood

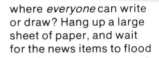

in—messages, remarks, drawings, anything you feel like. The whole family contributes:
"Has anybody seen my fountain pen?"—signed Father.
"Yes, I have put it back on your desk"—Anonymous.
"Can we have apple pie for dessert again soon?"
"You've already had it three times this week"—signed Mother.
Or if you feel inspired, what about a poem, a doodle, a portrait, a collage?

The sheets of paper should be as large as possible. Pin or tape them in a convenient place on the wall you have chosen (preferably in a room which you all use, like the bathroom or the hall). Within easy reach you should stock a box with pencils and different colored felt-tip pens, some glue and a pair of scissors, some brightly colored scraps of wrapping paper, etc.

The bottom of each sheet is reserved for the smallest members of the family. Once one sheet has been filled, hang a fresh sheet of paper on top (this will be page 2 of your newsletter). When five or six sheets have been filled, you can take them all down and staple them together into a family chronicle. If any of the individual newsletters is a real masterpiece, you can even preserve it for posterity by framing it!

when you're
alone

match tricks and games

Work these match tricks out for yourself first, and then have fun trying them out on your friends.

1. How many matches can you see in each of the two rows below? **Hint:** You are allowed to rearrange the matches in order to form words.

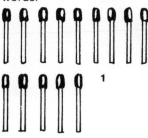

2. In (a) and (b) can you make both sides equal by moving *only* the matches to the left of the equal

sign? **Hint:** What does a multiplication sign look like? What does a division sign look like?

3. Can you make a square on the table with five matches?

4. By moving three matches only, make another triangle identical to one of the ones in the picture.

5. Without moving the equilateral triangle on the left, use the other three matches to make four triangles in all, each identical to the first one.

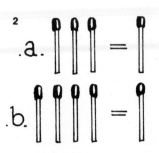

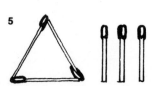

40

Answers

1. Were these the numbers you found?

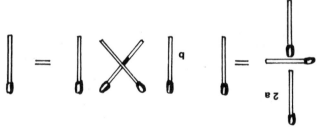

2. a) One divided by one equals one.

2. b) One multiplied by one equals one.

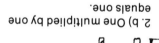

3. Take one of the matches in your fingers and use it to "make" a square out of the other four.

4. Take away three matches and make the triangle elsewhere. Nothing to it, is there?

5. The trick is to use the three matches to make the triangle into a pyramid. Stand one match at each corner and bring them together in the center. The flat surface of a pyramid consists of four equilateral triangles.

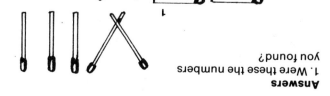

visiting hours

Here are some match games to play if a friend comes to see you.

five, four, three

You need 12 matches. Lay them out in three straight rows—5 in the first, then 4, then 3 (see sketch below).
The game begins: Take turns picking up matches. You can remove as many as you like at one time provided they are all in the same row.

The object is to try and get your opponent to pick up the *last* match.
The loser is the one who picks up the last match.

fifteen

This time you need 15 matches. Put them out on the table in any order you like.

Each of you is allowed to pick up either 1, 2, or 3 matches at a time.

You lose if it is your turn to play and there is only one match left on the table.

twelve in a row

Lay your 12 matches out side by side in a row. Space them all out evenly until you get to the twelfth match. Leave an extra space between the eleventh and twelfth (as shown in the diagram).

The object is to pick up the last match.

Play: You can either pick up 1 or 2 matches at a time (not more). But, if you take 2, they must be side by side without a gap in between.

For instance, you cannot pick up 11 and 1 together, but you can pick up 1 and 2, 2 and 3, and so on.

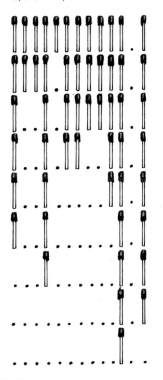

A mathematical morning

fun with figures

How to play: You always start off with the same six numbers (1–2–4–6–7–25), and you have to try and make them into whatever three-figure number you are given.

What you do: You can add, subtract, divide, and multiply the numbers to get your result, *provided* you use *all six* numbers and never the same one twice.

For example: Suppose you are given the number 460. There are several possibilities. Here are two:

1. 2 plus 1 equals 3; 3 times 7 equals 21; 21 plus 25 equals 46, 6 + 4 times 46 equals 460.
$[(2 + 1) \times 7 + 25 \times (6 + 4)] = 460$

2. 6 times 4 equals 24; 24 minus 1 equals 23; 25 plus 2 and minus 7 equals 20; 23 times 20 equals 460.
$[(6 \times 4) - 1] \times [25 + 2 - 7] = 460$.

How to play on your own
Write down any three-figure number that comes into your head. Can you combine the six numbers so that they make up the

number you want?
Example: 372
Answer: $[25 \times (7 + 6 + 2) - 4 + 1] = 372$.

With two or more people
One person chooses a three-figure number at random, and you all have to try and find the combination. This time it's a race, and the first one to find a valid solution is the winner.

Take turns chosing the number:

$476 = [(2 + 4 + 6 + 7) \times 25] + 1$
$452 = [(1 + 4 + 6 + 7) \times 25] + 2$

Count as you play

snap
solitaire

Take a pack of cards and remove all the cards from 2 through 6. Shuffle the 32 remaining cards. Start turning them up one by one, saying out loud each time, "7, 8, 9, 10, Jack, Queen, King, Ace," in that order, over and over again the whole way through the pack.

Snap!
Whenever the card you turn up is the same as the one you call out, you remove it from the pack. The idea is to try to get rid of all the cards in this way.
• If you do not have a single "Snap" the first time through, you lose.
• If, on the other hand, you have had one "Snap" or more, you can go on. Pick up the remaining

cards and start turning them over again, and so on until there are no more cards in the pack (well done, you win!), or until you get stuck (bad luck, you lose.) Beware! When you pick up the pack to start again, do not begin with the 7 each time, but go on calling out the cards from where you left off.

45

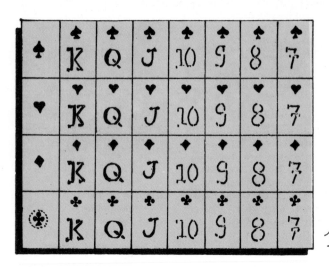

unlucky sevens solitaire

Take a pack of cards and remove all the cards from 2 through 6. Shuffle the remaining 32 cards well. Lay them out on the table face down in four rows of seven cards (see sketch 2 opposite). Keep the last four cards in your hand.

How to begin: Turn up any one of the cards on the table and find the space where it belongs according to the special order shown in sketch 1. Put it down face up, and as you do so, pick up the card which is lying in that space, look at it and put it in the space where *it* belongs. Keep playing in exactly the same way. For instance, suppose the first card you turn up is the King of Spades (see sketch 2). It belongs in the second space from the left in the top row. Before you put

down the King, you pick up the card that is there already, look at it, find the space for it, pick up the next one, and so on.

Beware of the sevens

The sevens all belong in the empty spaces at the far right of each row. Each time you turn up a 7 or find that the space where your card belongs is empty, you are forced to take a card from the four in your hand and to go on playing with that. *The object* of the game is to get *all* the cards face up in their right positions.

Stuck?

If you have used up all four cards and find that there are only a few cards still face down on the table, you can turn them up. If they happen to be in the right position, you win.

Exciting espionage

secret
codes

One morning you find a sealed envelope on your desk, marked "urgent." Inside it there is a message in code:

UOY WOHS OT GNIHTEMOS TOG EV'I. SSECER TA DNUORGYALP EHT NI EM TEEM*

Can you decipher it? Is it a trap? Should you reply? Suddenly you are plunged into the world of crime detection, espionage and counter-espionage. But you do not need to be called Sherlock Holmes or 007 to work out the message above. If you have not figured it out already, you will find a clue on page 50.

Beware of using an easy code too often. Your enemies will not be fooled by it for very long. If you don't want to be found out, keep several different codes up your sleeve. Practice them on your

friends until you are a real code expert. You will find quite a few to choose from in the pages that follow.

*MEET ME IN THE PLAYGROUND AT RECESS. I'VE GOT SOMETHING TO SHOW YOU.

mirror writing

Top speed and top secret! If you are in a hurry and want a quick, easy way of putting your message into code, why not simply write it back to front? There are several different ways you can do this.

Suppose you want to reply to the message on page 49 by saying: CAN'T MAKE IT TODAY. TEAM PRACTICE. You can either write the whole message back to front (as on page 49): ECITCARP MAET. YADOT TI EKAM T'NAC, *or* you can write each word back to front in the original order: T'NAC EKAM TI YADOT. MAET ECITCARP, *or* write each sentence back to front separately: YADOT TI EKAM T'NAC. ECITCARP MAET.

You will see that each version looks quite different.

invisible ink

This is one piece of equipment you cannot afford to be without. The magic formula is quite simple. See if you can find a lemon (or an onion if you do not mind shedding a few tears in the process). Squeeze it and use the juice as ink. You will need a fine paint brush or a matchstick to write with. Write your message on a piece of paper, and then let it dry out *gently* on a radiator or near an electric light bulb. Follow these instructions very carefully if you want your message to be really invisible.

To read what you have written, hold the paper over a candle flame (but not so close enough for it to catch fire!). The words will show up yellowish brown.

spiral writing   shift code

Take a piece of graph
paper and mark out a
square grid. The number
of squares on each side
must be odd, so that there
is a central square in the
middle of the grid. This is
where you begin: Write the
first letter of your message
in the central square, and
the rest in a spiral around
it—one letter in each
square all the way round,
(as shown in the diagram
below). Follow the arrow
to read the message.
Count the number of
letters in your message
before you start. Suppose
there are 52—you will need
a grid nine by nine
squares. It does not matter
if your message is too
short to fill the grid, but it
must not be too long or it
will not fit in.

Replace each letter of the
message you want to write
with the one that comes
directly before or after it in
the alphabet (or further
away still). When you send
the message you must
enclose a clue—this clue is
a number.
For instance: "4·+" means
that each letter in your
message has been shifted
forward four spaces, 4 +
HERKIV, NIIS SYX YJ
WMKLX, decoded, reads
DANGER KEEP OUT OF
SIGHT.

Your own shift rule
To simplify the coding
(and decoding!) of your
messages, you can write
out the alphabet clearly on
two separate strips of
paper. Line them up one
above the other and move
the bottom strip the
required number of spaces
each time. The letter below
the letter you want is now
the coded version.
**For really dangerous
missions,** use a variable
shift code. Try 1 + 2 + 3 +.
The first letter of the
message is shifted forward
one space, the second
two, the third, three, the
fourth *one,* the fifth two,
and so on.

A	M	Y	A	D	N	O
Y	R	I	B	Y	M	M
I	T	O	Y	N	O	N
F	H	U	C	A	T	O
A	D	C	O	M	E	Y
N	A	Y	P	A	R	T
C	Y	D	R	E	S	S

a number code in pictures

the more original the better.
Can you decode the name pictured below?

A 1	I 9	R 18
B 2	J 10	S 19
C 3	K.....11	T 20
D 4	L 12	U 21
E 5	M 13	V 22
F 6	N 14	W 23
G 7	O 15	X 24
H 8	P 16	Y 25
	Q.....17	Z 26

Write out all the letters of the alphabet in order and give each one a number from 1 to 26. From now on, each number represents a particular letter.
There is a separate code

$$/ = 1$$
$$O = 5$$

$$P = 16 = OOO/$$
$$= OO|||\grave{|}|||$$

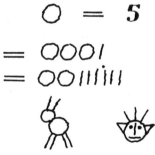

for the numbers: A straight line is worth 1; a circle is worth 5.
But it is much more fun if you make each number into a picture. The picture can be anything provided it has the right number of straight lines and circles—

10

15

19

5

16

8

53

the stencil code

A really good secret agent should never be without a stencil code. It is one of the most difficult to decipher, and the easiest to make—an ideal weapon in fact!

In a stencil code the letters of your message stand out from all the others around them only when you lay a special cut-out stencil on top. Without the stencil, the message cannot be decoded.

the swivel stencil

You need two sheets of graph paper, and a pocket-knife with a sharp blade to cut out the squares of the stencil. On the first sheet mark out a grid. The one in the sketch below has 36 squares. You will write your message on this first sheet. But first of all you must make the stencil. Mark out another grid exactly the same size as the first one on your second sheet of paper. Then cut out the nine squares in the places shown (diagram 1) on page 55 (the order is very important). Now lay the stencil on top of your original grid and start to

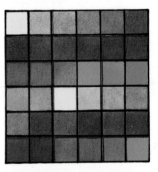

write your message on the bottom sheet of paper, putting one letter in each square which shows through a gap in the stencil. Start from the top left corner and work horizontally along to the end of each row, writing in a letter wherever there is a gap in the stencil. By the time you get to the bottom, you should have filled in nine letters.

Swivelling the stencil
Now turn the stencil 90 degrees to the left (see diagram 2). Nine more

empty squares will show up. Go on writing your message in exactly the

than 36 letters long, for example), you can design

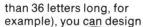

1

2

same way as before. Turn the stencil around 90 degrees a second and a third time until you have used up all the squares on your grid. Turn it a fourth time and the first letters of your message will appear.

ordinary stencils

If you do not want to use all the squares in the grid (if your message is less

your own stencil, cutting out as many squares as you need in whatever order you like.

Useful hints

When you turn your stencil, if you find that one of the squares has already been written in, just pass it up and go on to the next one.

When you decode the message, cross out the letters as you go. This will help you keep track of where you are.

secret scripts

One example of such a script is the ancient

Before they learned to write, people had no way of communicating over long distances. But after writing was invented, they soon found that the written word had certain drawbacks. Important messages and secrets could all too easily go astray or fall into the hands of an enemy—with disastrous results! A special way of writing secret messages had to be invented—this was called *crytography* (from the Greek, meaning secret writing).

Ever since then, codes or ciphers have been used by anybody with an important secret to transmit: armies, the Secret Service, gangsters, smugglers. At the same time other people are busy trying to "break" the codes as quickly as they are invented. These people are called decoding experts. Certain strange scripts exist, that are very difficult to read although they were not intended to be secret.

Egyptian hieroglyphics. The code had been lost and it was only in 1822, after years of research, that a Frenchman named Jean-Francois Champollion succeeded in deciphering them. It is not surprising that it took him a very long time when you consider that our own alphabet has only 26 letters, while *he* was examining more than 700 different signs!

Modern Chinese is rather like a secret code too. In all, there are more than 80,000 characters (or letters) in the written language (6000 to 8000 of these are in everyday use). People say that it takes a Chinese person twenty years to learn to read properly.

party
games

shadowy shapes

Why not put on a really spooky shadow play for your friends or family? A shadow theater is easy to make. Just stretch a sheet or a plain tablecloth between two chairs or in the frame of a door. You can anchor the corners with thumbtacks, or by tying them. The cloth must go right down to the floor (a pair of feet peeping out from underneath spoils the effect!). The audience sits in front of the screen and all the lights in the room are turned off, except for one, which you have carefully placed about six feet behind the screen. The light source can be a candle, a lamp, or a flashlight. Any person or object placed between the light and the screen will show up as a black silhouette on the screen itself. The stage is set and your play can begin.

If you prefer, you can divide the players into teams and make your theater the setting for a guessing game. Select some unusual objects and see if the others can recognize them by their shadows—in profile, or front view. (For example try a carving knife, a guitar, a spinning top, a sieve,

etc., or even one of yourselves back view, side view, or full face).
You may want to mime one of your favorite movie heros, or a story like the one above, which the others have to guess.

Use your shadow theater
to practice making animal
shadows like the wolf, the
rabbit, and the goat above.

a doorway theater

If you hang a blanket across the door frame so that the bottom reaches the ground and the top is at about shoulder level, you have a ready-made puppet theater.

You can make all sorts of different hand puppets out of cardboard, balls of wool, yogurt cartons, old socks, etc. You remain hidden behind the blanket, but the heads of your puppets show over the top.

one, two, three . . . fire!

If you run out of ideas, you can always use your puppet theater for some target practice. Use your puppets to fire at, or take turns walking behind the curtain with a hat on your head while the others take aim with ping-pong balls or balls of wool (no heavy ammunition allowed!).

A miniature amphitheater

the moving staircase

Here is a game which will keep you all on the move. You play on the stairs. The steps are your seats, but you never sit on the same one twice in a row! You take turns miming a short scene or incident in a story which you make up as you go along. Each scene has to follow the one before. Each time your turn comes around, you have to mime all the scenes which went before in the right order and without forgetting a single one (that's the tricky part). Then you mime your own contribution to the story, and so it goes on.

Take your seats

Sit down on the stairs one behind the other. The person on the bottom stair gets up and all the others move down one.

The curtain rises

He mimes a short scene:
• A man wakes up with a start.
Once he has finished, the actor climbs up to the top of the stairs and sits down behind the last member of the audience. The person sitting on the bottom step now stands up, while the rest of you all move down one again. This person has to mime the first scene plus one more, which he invents himself:
• A man wakes up with a start.
• He gets out of bed and begins looking for his slippers.
The third person has to mime the two previous scenes, plus his own, and so on.

You are eliminated if you forget a scene or get the order of scenes wrong. The game goes on until there is only one person left on the stairs, or until someone brings the story to a conclusive end.

multiple master-pieces

Feeling artistic? Put your talents to the test!
Pin a large sheet of paper to the wall or to a blackboard, and arm yourselves with a selection of colored pencils, chalks, or felt-tip pens.

Action!
The first person draws an outline (whatever happens to come into his head). The next one adds a few more strokes, the third does the same, and so on. **Beware! Each time you add to the drawing, you must make it look like something quite different.** Once the masterpiece is well and truly finished, the first person can say what he had in mind when he drew the original outline, and you can compare the end result with the original.

Colorful collages
You can play the same game using glue, scissors, old newspapers, buttons, strands of wool, scraps of material—anything you can find.

67

the blindfold obstacle race

Here's a game that will have everyone laughing by the end. But try to keep a straight face to begin with! Take a whole series of different objects—lamps, books, toys, glasses, etc.— and spread them out on the floor so that there is just enough room to step in between or over them. Now pick one of your friends (preferably one with a sense of humor!). Tell him that he has to walk blind-folded across the room, avoiding as many of the obstacles as possible.

Let him have a good look at the way they are arranged, and when he is ready, blindfold him, and tell him he can have a few moments to concentrate before beginning. Meanwhile the rest of you stealthily remove all the objects from his path. On "go" the person will set off gingerly picking his way in and out and over all sorts of imaginary obstacles . . . and this comic sight will soon have you all in fits of laughter!

puff and blow

You need two chairs, with a piece of string about six feet long stretched between them and tied to the back of each one, a small piece of tissue paper (about one inch by one inch), and—lots of puff! You can either play with one other person or in teams, with an equal number of people on either side of the string and one person to act as referee.

What you have to do is blow the tissue paper over the string into your opponents' court. There are no boundaries on the two sides but you are not allowed to set foot in the opposite court. You can either crouch or kneel on the ground, but **you must not stand up.** If necessary, you can put your hands on the floor to steady yourself, but you must never touch the paper with your hands.

The game begins: The referee drops the paper directly above the string, and both teams begin to puff and blow.

Scoring: 1 point—
• If you manage to get the paper to touch the ground on the other side.
• If your opponent blows it under the string in error.

Courting Lady Luck

a giant do-it-yourself dice game

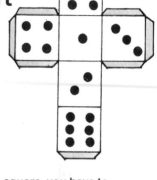

The board: Make a huge board out of a sheet of cardboard or wrapping paper (or draw it in chalk if you have a stone floor). Choose whatever shape you like. There should be at least 18 boxes, and each one must be numbered.

The dice: You need a giant dice to match. Make it out of a piece of stiff cardboard, as shown in the sketch above. The sides of the squares should be four inches long.

The counters: You each choose your own counter (a spoon, a pencil sharpener, a toy car, a tennis ball). It does not matter what it is, as long as each one is different.

The game is like most dice games. You throw to start, and play in turns, moving forward the same number of squares as the number you throw. But, for every square on the board there is a task—pleasant or unpleasant. It's up to you to decide what the task will be. Whenever you land in a square, you have to perform the appointed task for that square.

The tasks: These are the sort of things you might choose:

• Hop all the way around the room on one foot.

• Go to the square which corresponds to the month in which you were born (square one for January, etc.).

• Throw the dice again. You have a second turn.

• Find a spider and bring it back (it does not have to be real—a paper one or a drawing will do).

• Find a prize for the winner.

Before you begin complete your list of tasks and write it out clearly on a large sheet of paper or blackboard.

steeple chairs

On your mark, get set, and off you go—but not too fast! The object of this game is to complete a course as quickly as you can but you are not allowed to touch the "steeple chairs" with any part of your body *or* your clothing.

Make sure that all breakables have been put away before you begin. Your steeple chairs should be sturdy and big enough to crawl under. The course should have a starting and a finishing line and in between, chairs to climb over, under, or through, chairs to run around or weave in and out of—all without touching. The players decide beforehand what to do at each chair. You tackle the course one at a time. The others time you with a watch or count out loud.

But as you go, you must be thinking ahead all the time. If you touch anything or forget what to do at one of the steeple chairs, the others shout "*stop,*" and you have to go back to that chair again. Meanwhile time is running out, so you cannot afford to make too many mistakes.

A party game for Pinocchios

move
the chair

At your birthday party, you can ask your friends to *move a chair*. It sounds easy, but in fact this game needs a bit of preparation, and this is something you can do on your own beforehand.

What you do on your own

Take a piece of stiff cardboard and cut out enough cards all the same size for everyone to have two each (make a few extra to be on the safe side). Divide them into two equal piles:

On the cards in the first pile you draw *what* the person must move the chair with. Some possibilities for each card in the pile:

- One hand (sketch a)
- Two hands (b)

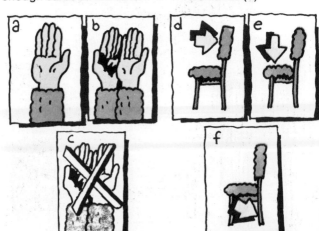

74

- No hands (c)
- Legs, feet, arms, chin, or even a nose—why not? There are heaps of possibilities and the same ones can be repeated any number of times.

On the cards in the second pile, you draw *where* the person must hold the chair in order to move it. Once again, you draw one possibility on each card:

- By the back (d)
- By the seat (e)
- By the leg (f), and so on.

The game can begin

Once you have all finished eating cake and ice cream, your friends will probably be ready for a bit of exercise. Pull out a chair, and decide how far you want it moved each time. The first person to play draws a card from each of the two piles. He immediately sees *what* he must move the chair with, and also *what part of the chair* he is allowed to touch in order to do so.

For example: Suppose he draws "No hands," and "by the seat." He can try hopping backwards on one foot, pulling the chair behind him with his other foot tucked under the seat. Or "No hands," and "by the back." That's not impossible either. He can push the chair along with his chest or arm pressing against the back.

If your game is a success, you can shuffle the cards and play another round.

75

A quiet game to play sitting down

peter and patrick

Each person must have a chair or a stool to sit on and you all sit in a circle. Suppose there are eight of you. Each of the eight places in the circle is given either a name or a number in this order: Peter, Patrick, 1, 2, 3, 4, 5, 6. **Peter begins:** He says, "Peter calls Patrick." It is Patrick's turn. He says, "Patrick calls 3"; 3 replies by calling another number or one of the two names, and so on. Each time the name or the number of the place where you are sitting is called, you have to answer by calling another name or number . . . and so on until . . . **someone makes a mistake** (by replying when it is *not* his turn, or not replying when it *is* his turn). This person now has to sit in place 6, and all the people before that number have to move around one place in a clockwise direction. If 2 makes a mistake he goes to 6; 6 to Peter, Peter to Patrick; Patrick to 1; 1 to 2. (3, 4 and 5 stay where they are.) Go on playing from where you left off. But don't forget your new number or name. If the person in seat number 6 makes a mistake, he changes places with Peter. The faster you play, the more fun it is.

76

Look sharp!

inventories

If you were making an inventory of all the objects in a room or house you would list everything from carpets to picture hooks. But our inventory is an alphabetical one. You choose a room and see if you can find 26 different objects in that room, each beginning with a different letter of the alphabet. There is a time limit, so you have to be quick!

Each player should have a sheet of paper and a pencil. Write the 26 letters of the alphabet down the left-hand side of the paper. Write in each object opposite the appropriate letter:

A—armchair
B—book
C—cupboard, and so on.

Two good tips:
• Whatever you do, don't touch anything in the room. That would only give the game away!
• If you get stuck on a letter, don't waste time. Go on to the next one.

Scoring:
You score one point for each object; the person with the most points wins. You can always move to another room and start again there!

a "quicky" for the quickest

Another alternative is to choose *one* letter of the alphabet and to see how many objects you can find in one room beginning with that letter. The time limit is much shorter this time. Once again you score a point for each object. If you are playing in the kitchen for example, and the letter you choose is *C* your list might include: clock, china, coffee, cocoa, colander, and so on.

The best liar wins

call my bluff

Two of you play, with a grown-up acting as referee. The referee makes out a list of difficult or unusual words beforehand, and you have to guess the meaning of each word in turn. But it doesn't matter if you don't know the meaning. With a little skill and some luck, you will be able to bluff the other person into thinking you do.

The referee announces the word. **One of three things can happen:**

1. Neither of you "accept" (that is, claim to know the meaning of the word). Neither of you scores.

2. You "accept," and your opponent (X) does not.

a. At this point X is free to "call your bluff," that is, to see if you really do know the true meaning of the word. If you *are* able to give the right meaning, you score 2 points. (Well done! it sometimes pays to be honest). If you are bluffing, however, X scores 5 points.

b. Suppose X is afraid that you *do* know the meaning of the word. He does not want you to win 2 points, and so he does not call your bluff. In this case you win 1 point (even if in fact you were bluffing all the time).

3. You "accept" and so does X. If neither of you dares call the other's bluff, you score 1 point each.

If only one of you calls the other's bluff, you are back to situation 2a. Two points to you if you are *not* bluffing; five to X if you are.

If you *both* call each other's bluff, and you *both give the right answer,* you score two points each. If *you are both bluffing,* you both lose five points.

If only one of you gives the right answer, and the other is bluffing, you are back to situation 2a. Two points to you if you are *not* bluffing, five to X if you are.

listen carefully!

This game is a musical quizz. You need a quizz master, a record player, some records, and a pencil and a piece of paper for each player.

The quizz master selects a certain number of records and thinks up a question to go with each one, such as: the name of the piece, the name of the composer, the country where the music was written, the names of the different musical instruments used, etc.

The quizz begins: The quizz master tells you what the question is and plays an extract from the record. You write down the answer and he then goes on to the next question. One point for every correct answer.

surprise quizz

This time the quizz master does not tell you what the question is before you have finished listening to the record. It can be something quite unexpected, such as, "Write down the words of the chorus," or, "Does the guitarist have a moustache?"

Take turns being quizz master.

a pantomime

You need at least four people, plus an organizer. The organizer has to think up a theme for each team or pair to mime. He then gives a separate role to each person in the team. **If there are four of you,** and the themes are "the race course," and "the operating room," the four roles would be: the horse, the jockey; the doctor and the patient. He writes each one on a separate sheet of paper and hands them out. **The pantomime begins:** One person gets up and starts miming his role. The other three have to try and recognize what it is he is miming. The moment one of them realizes that his own part fits in with the first person's mime, he must get up and join him. When the other two have guessed the theme, they stand up and mime their own theme. **If there are more of you,** the organizer chooses a theme with a lot of different parts.

81

Fibbing for fun

lie detection

Can *you* tell when someone is lying? You need at least four people to play. One person sits opposite the other three. The three players choose an unusual word from a dictionary and, one after the other, they each give a different explanation of its meaning.

Only one person is telling the truth, and it is up to the fourth person to find out which one it is. He plays on his own against the other three.

Beforehand the three conspirators choose their word carefully and prepare the three definitions they are going to give (one of which has to be true, of course). They do their best to make all three sound as convincing as possible.

The game begins: The word is *ocularist.*

"An ocularist," says Number One, "is somebody who does research into people's eyesight. The ocularist's discoveries and inventions are used by the *oculist,* who is, as you know, the person who actually looks after your eyes."

"I agree that the word has something to do with eyes," says Number Two, "because of the Latin *oculus* meaning an eye; but it does not have anything to do with real eyes. An ocularist is a person who makes glass eyes."

"Of course it has something to do with the Latin," says Number Three, "but have you never heard of the word *ocular,* meaning the eyepiece of an optical instrument or telescope? The eyepiece is the part you look through, and the person who makes it is an ocularist."

Which of these three do you believe?

Number One and Number Three are lying. Number Two gave the real meaning of the word.

Watch it grow

your family tree

First of all, make a huge tree out of cardboard or stiff paper. Paint it all sorts of bright colors or cover it with wrapping paper or material.

Now you can start to assemble the family. Look around for old photographs, drawings, or portraits of the different members of the family and pin them in place.
You can even paint in huge arrows in a contrasting color to show how the different branches of the family are linked: your grandparents; Great Aunt Harriet; Uncle George; your mother and father; your brothers and sisters. There should be room for everyone, including your pets.

Dream up a drama

one story leads to another

Making up stories, dressing up, and playing guessing games are all great fun. This game combines all three. You need at least six people to play—the more the merrier, as long as the number is one that can be divided by six. Split up into three groups with the same number of people in each one, and call yourselves Groups A, B, and C.

Each team has a particular task to fulfill within a given time limit (10 minutes). Group A thinks up a story, while Groups B and C wait outside. When the 10 minutes are up, Group B comes in and starts bombarding Group A with questions to try and find out what the story is about. But Group A can only answer "yes" or "no." Time's up! and Group B now has to mime the story as its players see it. This

time it is Group C that must guess. The players in Group C come back into the room and sit down. To make things easier for them, the actors dress up. They have 10 minutes to act their story. During this time Group C can ask any number of questions but the actors can only reply with a nod or a shake of their heads.

Time's up. Now, what is the story according to Group C? Compare their version with the original— the two will probably have very little in common. You will all want to have a turn at thinking up a story (A), at acting it (B), and at guessing (C), so trade roles the next time you play.

Scrumptious sweets and snacks

work up an appetite

A party is not a party without lots of good things to eat. But it is even more fun if you have made some of them yourself, and the cake, pudding, or drink that you have had a hand in preparing always tastes better than anything else.

A word of advice to cooks

• Don't leave your preparations until the last moment. Ask your mother well in advance if it's all right to use the kitchen.

• Before you do anything else, read the recipe carefully, and check that you have all the necessary ingredients and utensils.

• If you want to be allowed to cook another time, leave the kitchen absolutely spotless when you have finished.

Aprons on, and off you go!

chocolate truffles

fruit cup

For three to four people you need:

1 4-oz. block of milk (presweetened) chocolate
2 oz. butter or margarine
½ oz. confectioners sugar
1 egg yolk

Grate the chocolate into a bowl and put aside two tablespoonfuls. The butter should be soft, but not melted. Cut it into small pieces and add it to the chocolate. Stir with a wooden spoon. Add the sugar, and keep stirring until you have a smooth paste. Still stirring, add the egg yolk and mix thoroughly. Let the mixture stand for 10 minutes. Using your fingers, shape it into small balls the size of a large marble. Roll each one carefully in the extra chocolate. Leave your truffles in a cool place to set.

For eight to ten people you need:

1 banana
2 oranges
2 peaches
1 lemon
12 oz. grape juice
12 oz. orange juice
12 oz. lemonade

Take a large mixing bowl or a soup tureen and cut the fruit into it. Peel and slice the banana, peel the oranges and cut in round slices. Skin the peaches and cut them into very small pieces.
Grate the rind of the lemon and squeeze out the juice. Sprinkle the grated rind and lemon juice over the fruit. Pour the grape juice and the orange juice over the fruit, and let stand in a cool place. Chill the lemonade thoroughly and add it at the last moment.

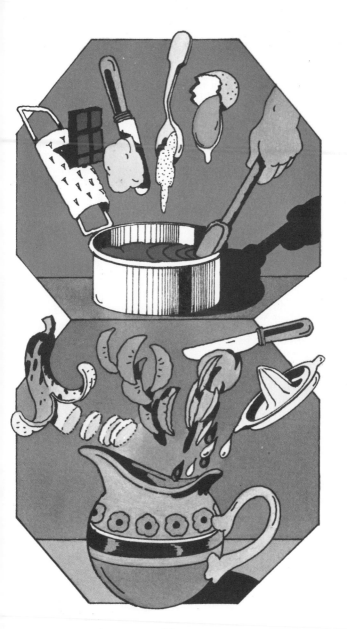

bring the fruit to life

Turn your fruit bowl into a regular Noah's ark! With a little imagination and a few odds and ends, you can make all sorts of amusing animals to surprise your friends. Toothpicks, coffee beans, lady fingers, candied fruit, maraschino cherries, and a leaf or two will all help.

The plum-headed apple-sheep: An apple and a plum stuck together, four toothpicks for the legs, coffee beans for the nose and eyes.

The pear-shaped rabbit: Remove the stem and set the pear on its wider end. Stick in two lady fingers for the ears and coffee beans for the eyes and nose. A maraschino cherry for the tail.

The apple-almond giraffe: The giraffe's head is an almond, with a toothpick forced into it to form the long neck. The body is an apple. To keep the giraffe from toppling over, you can press the four toothpick legs into a slice of bread.

For a winter's day
orange fruit salad

The ingredients are:

5 oranges
6 oz. black grapes
8 oz. confectioners sugar

Wash one of the oranges carefully and, without peeling it, slice it into rounds. Peel the other four oranges and cut them into quarters. Arrange the orange rounds and quarters carefully in a big bowl (a glass one, if you want your salad to be a show piece). Sprinkle the grapes on top. Put the sugar in a saucepan with a cup (8 oz.) of water. Stir well and bring to a boil. Let it boil for about five minutes. Now pour the hot liquid over the fruit in the bowl. Let cool. This orange salad should be eaten well chilled. Serves four.

To cure a cold

home-made honey candy

You don't need to have a cold to enjoy these delicious honey flavored hard candies. You will need:

1½ cups crystallized sugar
2 tablespoons honey
1 teaspoon orange flower water
A large sheet of waxpaper

Put the sugar into a large saucepan. Add half a glass of warm water, then the honey and the orange flower water. Boil the mixture rapidly until it begins to change color. The liquid should form a long sticky thread if you dip in a spoon and lift it up. Hold the spoon over the sheet of grease-proof paper and drop small amounts of the mixture onto it. Each drop is a piece of candy. Wait until they are quite cold before you remove them from the paper.

cheese straws

The recipe for these cheese straws is so simple that you can't go wrong. You need:

1 cup all-purpose flour
4 level tablespoons butter, or margarine
5 tablespoons grated Cheddar cheese
2 tablespoons milk
½ teaspoon salt

Mix all the ingredients together in a large bowl until you have a firm, smooth dough. Roll the dough out flat with a floured rolling pin. Now cut it into long, narrow strips. Cut each strip into smaller pieces, and lay them out on a flat cooky sheet. Bake the straws in a medium hot oven (400°F.) for 10 to 15 minutes. When they are done, they should be a nice golden brown color. Keep one or two for your parents to taste before supper!

a summer fruit

a winter fruit

In the summer, when apricots are in season, make yourself a little whistle out of an apricot pit. Rub the two flat ends of the pit with a nail file or a piece of sandpaper until two little holes appear. Keep rubbing until the holes are big enough for you to remove the inner seed with a pin. Now you have a whistle.
Hold it between your lips and your teeth and blow into the holes. In the south of France where this sort of whistle comes from, people use them to imitate all sorts of bird songs.

Grow a lemon tree in your home. For the pot you need a small plastic container like a yogurt or a sour cream carton. Make two holes in the bottom for the water to run through, and stand the pot on a saucer or on a jam-jar lid. Take four or five seeds from a good fresh lemon, and put them in the pot with a little earth, which you should break up carefully with your fingers. Stand the pot in a warm place and water it whenever the earth begins to look dry and parched. When your lemon tree begins to get too big for its pot, you will need to transfer it to a larger one.

a recipe with a touch of magic

You will be surprised how quick and easy this fruit jelly is to make.
Use raspberries, red currants, or black currants, whichever you prefer. Put on a large apron, as you may get rather sticky. Wash the berries thoroughly before you start. Put them in the middle of a clean cloth (which you are sure will not be needed again). Hold the cloth by the four corners and begin twisting it with both hands, working towards the middle. Put a large bowl underneath to catch the juice as you squeeze it out through the cloth. Weigh the juice on a kitchen scale (weigh the empty basin first, then with the juice in it—the difference between the two is the weight of the juice). Add an equal weight of sugar. Heat the juice and sugar in a saucepan over a low heat for about 10 minutes, stirring gently all the time. Abracadabra. It has turned into a thick jelly, which you can pour into a jam jar and let cool.

Learn to recognize

A Panda Paperback

...and open the doors to adventure and fun with the latest how-to-do-it guides to your favorite crafts and hobbies, sports and games.

Be sure to look for:

FUN WITH YARN
New and exciting craft projects for non-knitters

KITES!
Instructions for making and flying kites from all over the world

PLAYHOUSES, CABINS, AND TENTS
Plans for designing and building treehouses and huts

FUN WITH CLAY
Easy modeling projects for everything from animals to jewelry

FUN WITH PHOTOGRAPHY
Easy-to-follow instructions to exciting photo projects and basic camera techniques

TRAVEL GAMES
Exciting games and activities to keep you amused on the longest journey

GAMES FOR A RAINY DAY
Indoor activities for every occasion...games to play alone or with friends at a party

FUN WITH PUPPETS
Instructions for easy-to-make puppets, marionettes and shadow theaters

Published by:
FRANKLIN WATTS, INC.
730 Fifth Avenue
New York, N.Y. 10019

Printed in France by Imprimerie Tardy Quercy Auvergne, Bourges